P9-DCX-864

50

THINGS TO SEE WITH A

TELESCOPE

KIDS

And Parents, too!

By John A. Read

This book is dedicated to the wonderful
folks at the Halifax Centre of the Royal
Astronomical Society of Canada.

www.facebook.com/50ThingstoSeewithaSmallTelescope

Final copy edits, formatting, and design by Kurtis Anstey. Content edit by Dave Chapman.

Telescope view source files for deep-sky objects were constructed from actual photos taken by the author, either using his personal four-inch refractor, twelve-inch Dobsonian and eight-inch Dobsonian, or using the following remote observatories: Abbey Ridge Observatory (owned by Dave Lane), and the Burke-Gaffney Observatory at Saint Mary's University, Halifax. These images were then processed to simulate a visual observation. Exceptions include M1, imaged by Kurtis Anstey; Comet C/2013 US10, imaged by Dave Lane; M81, M82, and the Double Cluster, by Stuart Forman; and, M41, by Tom Ruen. Image of the Northern Hemisphere is derived from an image created by Daniel R. Strebe downloaded 8/03/2017

Star maps used in this book were sourced using Stellarium, an open-source stargazing program. These maps were then customized using various software programs for the purpose of this book. Stellarium is the best astronomy software out there (and it's free). A link to this software can be found here: http://stellarium.org

Special thanks to artist Johan Meuris for creating the constellation art used in Stellarium. Several of his images are included in this book. Usage rights for this work are detailed here: http://artlibre.org/licence/lal/en/

Images from NASA follow NASA's photo usage guidelines, found here: http://www.nasa.gov/audience/formedia/features/MP_Photo_Guidelines.html

Image of Comet 67P credit: ESA/Rosetta/NAVCAM, CC BY-SA IGO 3.0

Image of Celestron FirstScope dobsonian compliments of Celestron. Image of Explore Scientific FirstLight refractor compliments of Explore Scientific

About the Author:

John Read began his stargazing experience as a child in the 1990s, but always found the hobby particularity challenging (mainly because his father's telescope wasn't very good). In 2012, his wife bought him a new telescope, and he joined the Mount Diablo Astronomical Society (MDAS) in California.

During his time with MDAS, John volunteered at hundreds of stargazing events, teaching children of all ages how to use telescopes and find objects in the night sky.

He used this opportunity to simplify the beginner stargazing experience, sharing this knowledge in his first book, *50 Things to See with a Small Telescope*.

John is now a full-time Astrophysics student at Saint Mary's University, in Halifax, Nova Scotia. He can be found throughout the year volunteering at the Burke-Gaffney Observatory, and with the Halifax Centre of the Royal Astronomical Society of Canada.

John A. Read photographing the deep-sky objects explored in this book.

Note to Parents

Astronomy is a challenging hobby, and the introduction is something you'll want to do together, with your kids, if they're going to find success and enjoyment. Here are a few things you can do to ensure a smooth introduction to the hobby:

- Read the telescope's manual, and learn how to use the telescope properly.
- Use this book to learn the night sky *without* the use of the telescope. Lay on your back under the stars and try to point out the constellations specific to the season.
- Help your kids learn to adjust their eyes to the dark. This means no flashlights, cell phones, porchlights, or car lights, **for at least thirty minutes** before attempting to view objects like galaxies, globular clusters, and nebulae, through a telescope.
- For the <u>absolute best</u> views, *with and without a telescope*, get at least thirty miles (fifty kilometers) away from city lights. Also, be aware that the moon phase will affect your stargazing experience. Viewing deep-sky objects (galaxies, globular clusters, and nebulae) is extremely difficult when the Moon is full, or nearly full.
- Understand that seeing many of the objects, especially galaxies, requires patience, and not all viewing attempts will be successful.

<u>WARNING</u>. Never use a telescope to look at the Sun, or use a telescope when there is the risk that the telescope might be pointed at the Sun*. Doing so would cause immediate and permanent blindness!

*Commercial solar filters are available for most telescopes. However, these should be used with extreme caution, especially when children are present.

CONTENTS

Telescopes for kids

Amateur astronomy is a challenging hobby, even for an adult. The targets in this book <u>are beyond the range of **toy telescopes**</u>. In general, the best scopes for beginners are either Dobsonians, or refractors on solid alt/az (up/down-left/right) mounts. Here are a few things you'll want to look for in a telescope:

How can you tell if a telescope is a toy? Point it straight up. If the tripod won't allow this, it won't be any fun for stargazing.

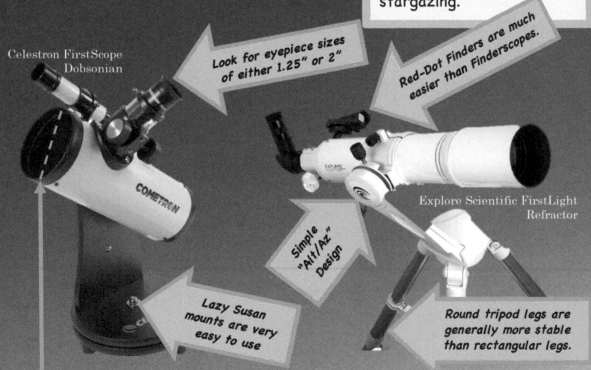

Celestron FirstScope Dobsonian

Look for eyepiece sizes of either 1.25" or 2"

Red-Dot Finders are much easier than Finderscopes.

Explore Scientific FirstLight Refractor

Simple "Alt/Az" Design

Lazy Susan mounts are very easy to use

Round tripod legs are generally more stable than rectangular legs.

In general, the aperture (the width of the mirror or lens), NOT the magnification, determines how much you'll be able to see.

Avoid telescopes on flimsy or camera tripods. These telescopes may be marketed to kids, but they are extremely challenging to point at objects in space.

Getting Started – Parts of a Telescope

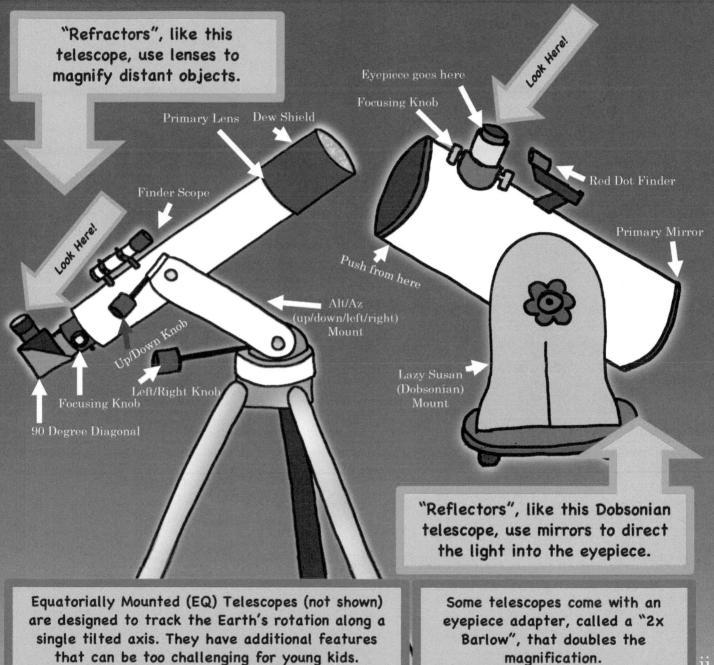

"Refractors", like this telescope, use lenses to magnify distant objects.

Look Here!

Eyepiece goes here

Focusing Knob

Look Here!

Primary Lens

Dew Shield

Finder Scope

Look Here!

Red Dot Finder

Primary Mirror

Push from here

Alt/Az (up/down/left/right) Mount

Up/Down Knob

Left/Right Knob

Focusing Knob

90 Degree Diagonal

Lazy Susan (Dobsonian) Mount

"Reflectors", like this Dobsonian telescope, use mirrors to direct the light into the eyepiece.

Equatorially Mounted (EQ) Telescopes (not shown) are designed to track the Earth's rotation along a single tilted axis. They have additional features that can be too challenging for young kids.

Some telescopes come with an eyepiece adapter, called a "2x Barlow", that doubles the magnification.

Focusing your telescope

In order to see anything through your telescope, it must be in focus. To do this, point the telescope at the moon or a bright star. Then, twist the focus knob until the image of the moon is sharp, or the star is as small as you can make it.

In Focus GOOD!

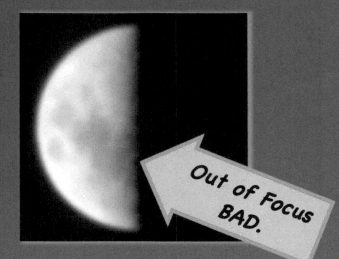

Out of Focus BAD.

Use this one!

Choosing your eyepiece

Most telescopes come with two eyepieces, one with a larger lens (more glass) than the other. The eyepiece with the larger lens is the one you want to use most of the time. Only use the smaller one when you want to "zoom in" on a target like a planet. Remember, the most important thing is light gathering, **not magnification.**

Finding objects in the night sky

1) Using this book or astronomy software, determine if your target is visible.
2) Find the object's position without the telescope.
3) Use the finder scope to point the telescope.
4) View the object through the telescope's eyepiece.

For objects like galaxies, nebulae, and globular clusters, viewing the object can still be a challenge, and may take multiple nights and lots of practice.

Pointing your telescope For a telescope to work properly, the finder scope (or red-dot finder) must be "aligned" so that it points at exactly the same place as the telescope. To do this, point the telescope at a bright star. Twist the alignment knobs on the finder scope until the star is centered in **both** the finder scope, and the telescope.

How to look through the telescope Touching the telescope when viewing makes it shake, and prevents you from appreciating the object you are trying to see. Don't touch the telescope AT ALL when observing an object. Hold your eye just above the eyepiece and put your hands behind your back.

Adapting your eyes to the dark Viewing objects like galaxies, nebulae, and globular clusters also requires you to prepare your eyes. It takes about 30 minutes to adapt your eyes to see these objects.

This means you can't look at car headlights, porch lights, or cell phones. It also means NO FLASHLIGHTS*, or even looking at the Moon.

*Exception: Cover a flashlight with red cellophane, this helps keep your eyes adapted to the dark.

What are Dark Skies?

Many of the objects in this book are fairly bright, and can be seen as long as it is the correct season, and the clouds aren't in the way. However, some galaxies, nebulae, and globular clusters require dark, or very dark skies.

Poor Sky	Fair Sky	Dark Sky	Very Dark Sky
In a town, or during a full Moon.	Suburban skies, 10 miles from the nearest town.	Country skies, 20 miles from the nearest town.	50 miles from the nearest town.

The Whirlpool Galaxy (M51) viewed under different sky conditions.

To find a very dark sky near you, visit:
http://darksitefinder.com/maps/world.html

A sky for all seasons

Hopefully you know that the Earth revolves around the Sun. This fact has a fascinating consequence in astronomy. Depending on where the Earth is in its orbit determines what stars can be seen on a given night. This is because we can't see stars on the other side of the Sun!

For this reason, stars and other deep sky objects in this book will be divided up by season.

Autumn Sky

Summer Sky

The Sun

Winter Sky

Spring Sky

This book assumes you're living in the Northern Hemisphere vi

If you look up at the night sky for any length of time, you'll notice that the stars appear to rotate around the North Star. A complete rotation occurs about once every day, as the Earth spins, and about once every year, as the Earth revolves around the Sun.

Spring

Winter

The Big Dipper

The North Star

Summer

Autumn

NORTH

Observing the Big Dipper around 11 PM, each season.

For this reason, objects near the North Star never dip below the horizon*, and can be viewed all year long. These objects are referred to as "circumpolar".

* This book assumes you are in the Northern Hemisphere.

Finding the planets

Because planets wander across the sky from night to night, and month to month, it's difficult to display their location in a book. However, this is an extremely easy task for a computer.

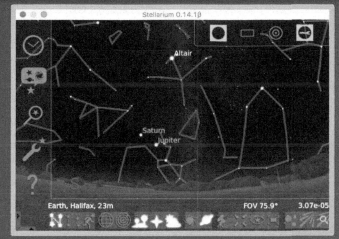

I recommend downloading a free program called Stellarium, available at Stellarium.org, or from the app store. After setting your current location and time, finding the position of the planets using this software is easy! Alternatively, explore any bright objects residing on the ecliptic (described below). If it's bright, and seems out of place, there's a good chance it's a planet.

Planets found here

Planets found here

Planets found here

Eastern Horizon

Western Horizon

Looking South*

Did you know? The Ecliptic is the path the planets, Moon, and the Sun take as they travel through the sky.

Getting Started – Deep-Sky Objects

Most of the telescope targets in this book are **"deep-sky"** objects. These targets reside outside our solar system (our solar system includes our Sun, the eight planets, and several dwarf planets like Pluto). Deep-Sky objects are tens of thousands, or even millions, of light-years away (one light year is about 9,500,000,000,000 kilometers)!

Spiral galaxy viewed "edge-on"

Spiral galaxy viewed "face-on"

Galaxies are clusters of millions, billions, or even trillions of stars. They also contain lots of gas and dust. Our home galaxy, the Milky Way, is visible as a cloud of stars that crosses the entire night sky. Most of the galaxies mentioned in this book are "spiral galaxies", and are viewed either "edge on" or "face-on".

Open Clusters are groups of stars that formed together at around the same time. Over millions and billions of years, these stars spread out across the galaxy.

Nebulae are giant clouds of gas and dust. Some nebulae are formed during supernovae, when a star explodes. Others are formed when a smaller star blows off its outer layers near the end of its life. Nebulae are also the place where stars are born.

Globular Clusters are tight groups of old stars orbiting our galaxy in a region called "the Halo". Our galaxy has over 150 of globulars. The closest globular clusters (M4 and NGC 6397) to Earth are 7,200 light-years away.

To find any object in the night sky, you'll have to plot a route! Imagine you're giving directions to the nearest store. You might say, "turn right at the traffic signal, and left at the stop sign." The same strategy works in the night sky. An astronomer might say: "follow the pointer stars to the North Star. Then, hop over to the Big W. You'll find the Dragonfly near the bottom left star in the W." This may sound confusing, but it will come naturally as you learn the constellations and bright stars.

Plotting a Route

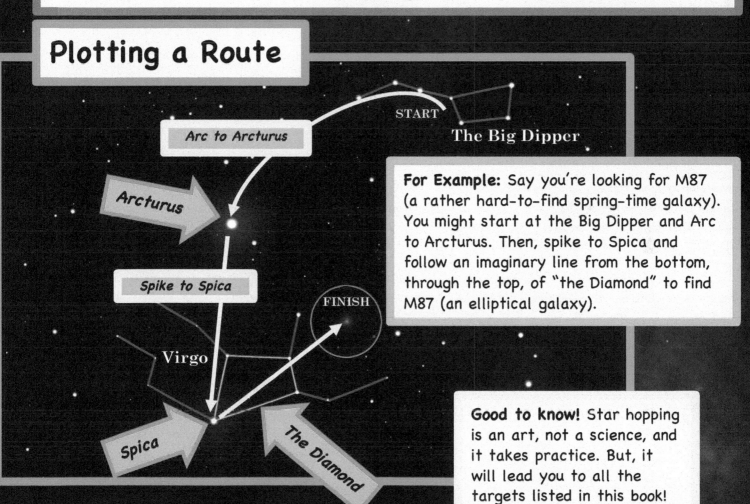

For Example: Say you're looking for M87 (a rather hard-to-find spring-time galaxy). You might start at the Big Dipper and Arc to Arcturus. Then, spike to Spica and follow an imaginary line from the bottom, through the top, of "the Diamond" to find M87 (an elliptical galaxy).

Good to know! Star hopping is an art, not a science, and it takes practice. But, it will lead you to all the targets listed in this book!

X

The Moon completes a full cycle through its phases about once every 29 days. Each night, the Moon's phase is slightly different.

DIFFICULTY ●○○○○

The Full Moon as viewed through a small telescope or binoculars

The Moon viewed at the same time each evening.

Night 7

First-Quarter Moon

Gibbous Moon

Crescent Moon

Night 1

Night 14

Full Moon

New Moon

Eastern Horizon   Southern Horizon   Western Horizon

After the Full Moon, the Moon "wanes" through the following phases: Waning Gibbous, Third Quarter, Waning Crescent, and then back to New Moon.

*As viewed from the Northern Hemisphere

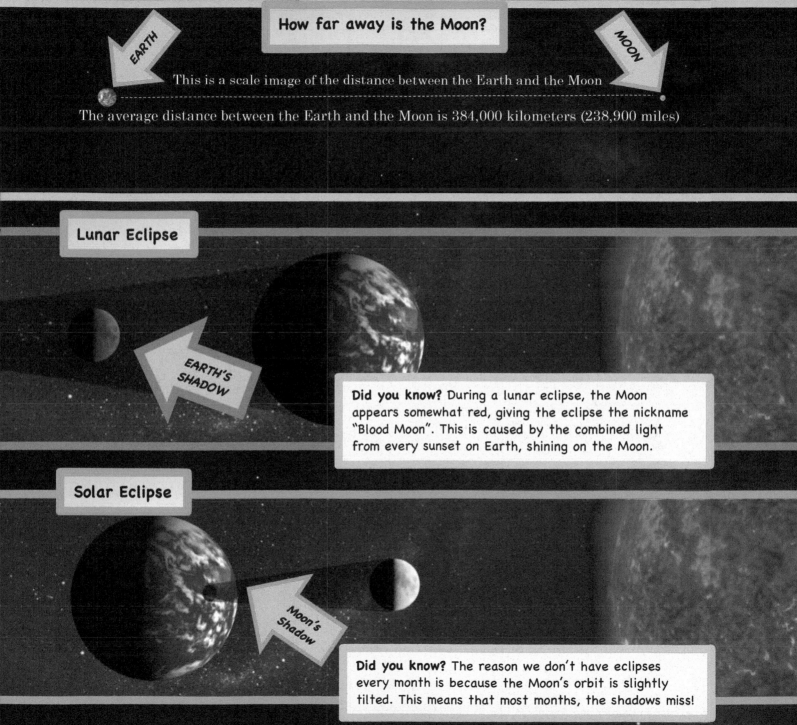

How far away is the Moon?

EARTH

MOON

This is a scale image of the distance between the Earth and the Moon

The average distance between the Earth and the Moon is 384,000 kilometers (238,900 miles)

Lunar Eclipse

EARTH'S SHADOW

Did you know? During a lunar eclipse, the Moon appears somewhat red, giving the eclipse the nickname "Blood Moon". This is caused by the combined light from every sunset on Earth, shining on the Moon.

Solar Eclipse

Moon's Shadow

Did you know? The reason we don't have eclipses every month is because the Moon's orbit is slightly tilted. This means that most months, the shadows miss!

The Big Dipper

CIRCUMPOLAR

The Big Dipper is the most recognizable shape in the night sky. The Dipper is circumpolar, meaning that it stays above the horizon for most people living in the Northern Hemisphere. The stars in the Big Dipper make great targets to explore with your telescope. In very dark skies you might spot a galaxy or two along the way!

The Surfboard Galaxy (M108)

DIFFICULTY ○○○○○

Did you know? The Big Dipper is not a constellation. It is a pattern of stars within the constellation Ursa Major (the greater bear). These star patterns are called "asterisms".

Because the North Star is circumpolar (or literally polar) it is visible all year! And, it stays in exactly the same place in the sky. Despite a popular misconception, the North Star is actually only the 48th brightest star in the sky.

The North Star

Find the North Star by following these two "pointer" stars in the Big Dipper.

The Big Dipper

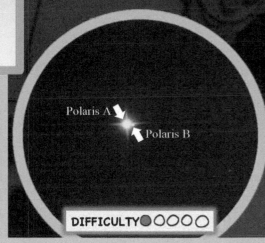

Polaris A

Polaris B

DIFFICULTY ● ○ ○ ○ ○

Through a telescope, you may be able to see a companion star, Polaris B

DID YOU KNOW? This star is important for sailors navigating at sea. The angle between this star and the horizon, multiplied by 69, provides the sailor their distance (in miles) from the equator!

Mizar and Alcor (nicknamed the "Horse and Rider") make up the center of the handle of the Big Dipper. Both Mizar and Alcor are visible without a telescope. What makes them interesting is that through a telescope, you'll notice that Mizar is also two stars!

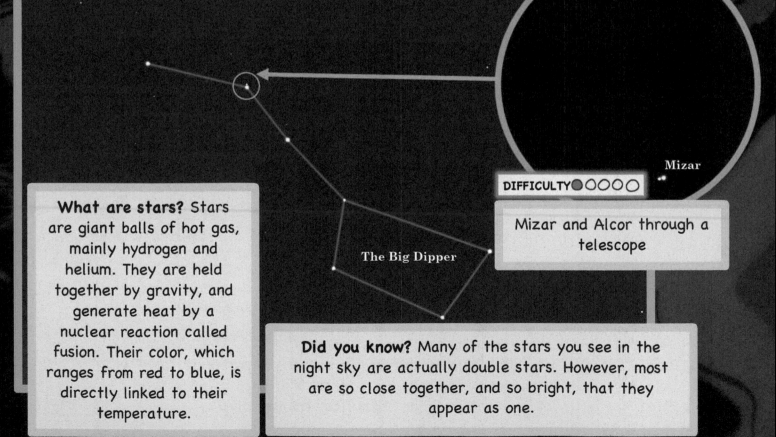

Alcor

Mizar

The Big Dipper

DIFFICULTY ● ○ ○ ○ ○

Mizar and Alcor through a telescope

What are stars? Stars are giant balls of hot gas, mainly hydrogen and helium. They are held together by gravity, and generate heat by a nuclear reaction called fusion. Their color, which ranges from red to blue, is directly linked to their temperature.

Did you know? Many of the stars you see in the night sky are actually double stars. However, most are so close together, and so bright, that they appear as one.

The Whirlpool and Pinwheel

These two galaxies located near the Big Dipper make great targets for winter, spring, and summer (they are a bit low in the sky in the fall). If you're near a town or city, if the Moon is up, or if you've not adapted your eyes to the dark, the Pinwheel may be invisible, but in dark skies it's a beautiful sight.

DIFFICULTY ●●●●●

The Pinwheel Galaxy (M101) is visible through a small telescope in **extremely dark skies** (make sure your eyes are well adjusted to the dark).

Galaxies (and globular clusters, too) often look dim and blurred, mainly due to imperfect sky conditions. Astronomers call these views, "beautiful smudges".

The North Star

The Big Dipper

The Whirlpool Galaxy (M51) is brighter than M101, and easier to find, even in light polluted skies.

DIFFICULTY ●●●○○

Because the stars in the Little Dipper are quite dim, it can be a challenge to identify. Start by finding the North Star at the end of the handle, and work your way over to the cup.

This pair of galaxies near the Big Dipper is visible through a small telescope almost every clear night. You should be able to see both galaxies at once.

The Little Dipper

The North Star

The Big Dipper

Cigar Galaxy (M82)

Bode's Nebula (M81)

DIFFICULTY ●●●○○

The Little Dipper is a nickname for the constellation Ursa Minor, which means "Little Bear".

Cassiopeia (or, the Big W) is always found on the opposite side of the North Star from the Big Dipper. Knowing how to find the Big W will lead to several other targets in the book, such as the Andromeda Galaxy and the Dragonfly Cluster.

In Greek mythology, Cassiopeia is a vain queen, obsessed with her own beauty

The North Star

The Big W
(Cassiopeia)

The Big Dipper

Fun Fact: As the Earth spins, the sky appears to rotate around the North Star. For this reason, the Big W may appear on any side of the North Star depending on the time of night.

DIFFICULTY ● ● ● ○ ○ ○

Open Star Cluster M103 is found within the Big W

Looking closer at the Big W, you will find plenty of interesting star patterns. The most fun cluster to see through a telescope is the Dragonfly. Recently, this cluster has become known as the E.T. Cluster, named after the alien from the Steven Spielberg film, E.T. The Extraterrestrial.

The Dragonfly, (A.K.A the E.T. Cluster) through a telescope

DIFFICULTY ●●○○○○

The Big W
(Cassiopeia)

The two bright stars are said to represent E.T.'s eyes.

In the dim constellation Camelopardalis, lies a beautiful chain of stars named after Father Lucian Kemble, a Canadian priest. Because Camelopardalis is difficult to identify, you'll want to use the Big W (Cassiopeia) as a guide.

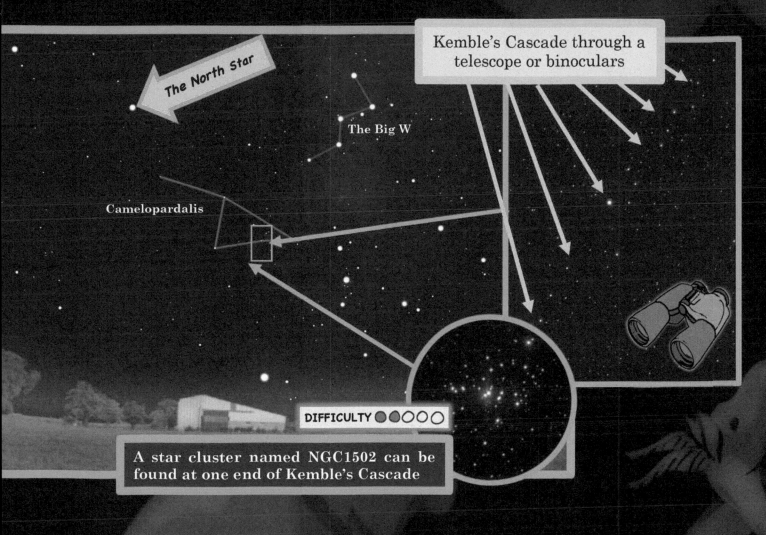

The North Star

The Big W

Kemble's Cascade through a telescope or binoculars

Camelopardalis

DIFFICULTY ●●○○○

A star cluster named NGC1502 can be found at one end of Kemble's Cascade

WINTER

Gemini (or "the Twins", as you can see by their constellation lines) is found near Orion in the winter. It is typically identified by locating the two top stars, Pollux and Castor.

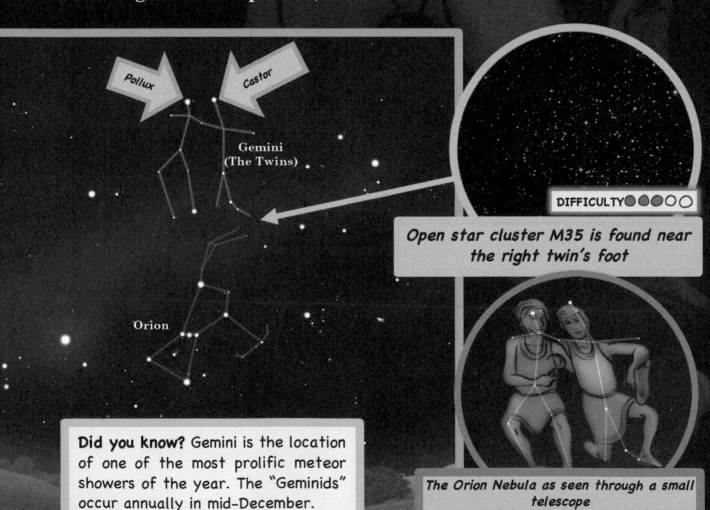

Pollux

Castor

Gemini
(The Twins)

Orion

DIFFICULTY ⬤⬤⬤◯◯

Open star cluster M35 is found near the right twin's foot

The Orion Nebula as seen through a small telescope

Did you know? Gemini is the location of one of the most prolific meteor showers of the year. The "Geminids" occur annually in mid-December.

Orion is the most prominent winter constellation. It is easily recognized by the three stars that make up Orion's Belt.

The red star near the top of the constellation is named Betelgeuse, while the bottom-right star, a blueish white star, is named Rigel.

Betelgeuse

Orion's Belt

Rigel

Orion is a hunter from Greek mythology

Fun Fact: This constellation is home to the famous Horsehead Nebula. This object is outside the range of the small telescope, but it makes a great target for astrophotographers. (Image credit: Ken Crawford)

The Great Nebula in Orion is arguably the most brilliant nebula in the sky. Located just below Orion's Belt, it's also the easiest to find.

The Orion Nebula can even be distinguished without a telescope. It is visible as a smudge of light in Orion's Sword.

This nebula is a great target for binoculars, too!

Orion's Belt

Orion's Sword

DIFFICULTY ●●○○○

The Orion Nebula as seen through a small telescope

The Crab Nebula is the remains of an exploded star. The event, called a supernova, was observed by Chinese astronomers in the year 1054.

Taurus

Taurus' left horn

Orion

DIFFICULTY ●●●●○○

The Crab Nebula is located beside the bright star that represents the left horn in Taurus, the Bull.

Canis Major, or as I like to call him, "the dog". In Greek mythology, this dog is following Orion, the hunter from the previous section.

Can you still see Orion?

Sirius

Open cluster M41 through a telescope

The bright star in the dog's neck is called Sirius. This is the brightest star in the night sky!

DIFFICULTY ●●○○○

Taurus means "the bull" in Latin. It's a prominent winter constellation. The brightest star in Taurus is Aldebaran, which also lies at one corner of the Hyades, the star cluster at the center of the constellation.

Can you still see Orion?

Taurus

The Pleiades

Aldebaran

The Hyades is the closest open star cluster to Earth. This makes it a great target for binoculars or small telescopes. The bright star, Aldebaran, is not actually part of the cluster!

DIFFICULTY ● ○ ○ ○ ○

This open cluster is easily visible without a telescope in late autumn evenings and throughout the winter. Due to its shape, many people mistakenly believe this is the Little Dipper.

Through a telescope, the stars appear brilliantly bright. Without a telescope, only six or seven stars are visible; but with a telescope, you'll see hundreds!

Taurus

Orion

DIFFICULTY ● ○ ○ ○ ○

Through a telescope or binoculars, the Pleiades appear as a brilliant cluster of dozens of stars

Perseus lies between the Big W (Cassiopeia) and Taurus (the constellation containing the Pleiades and the Hyades). Perseus is most famous for the Perseid Meteor Shower that occurs in mid-August. However, in the summer, Perseus doesn't rise until after midnight, so you'll have to stay up late to see the best shooting stars.

DIFFICULTY ●●●○○

The Spiral Cluster (M34)

Perseus

Here are the Hyades and the Pleiades, again!

Can you still see the Big W?

Perseus is named after a great hero in Greek mythology

WINTER

Some star clusters may not look like much, but, just like constellations, people have imagined patterns within them and given them names. M38 is known as the Starfish Cluster. I like to call M37 "the Cloaking Warbird", after the Romulan starship from Star Trek!

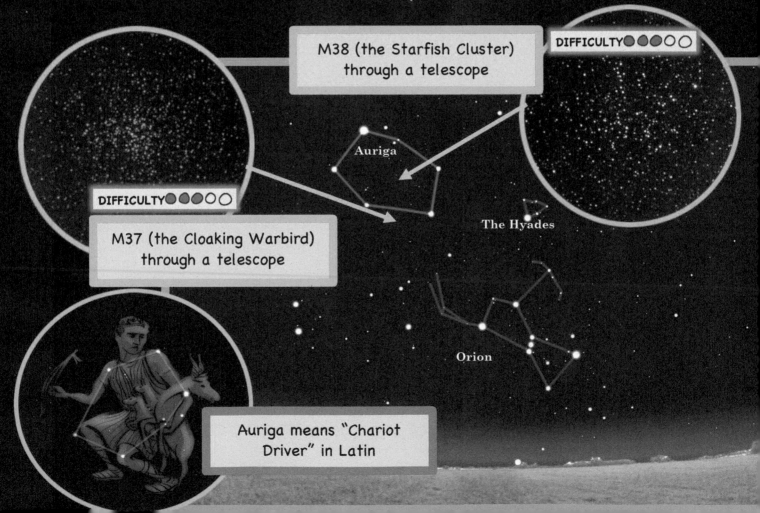

M38 (the Starfish Cluster) through a telescope

DIFFICULTY ● ● ● ○ ○

Auriga

The Hyades

DIFFICULTY ● ● ● ○ ○

M37 (the Cloaking Warbird) through a telescope

Orion

Auriga means "Chariot Driver" in Latin

During the winter, a star pattern called "The Winter Hexagon" will help orient you, helping you identify the nearby constellations. The hexagon is formed by joining the stars: Rigel, Aldebaran, Capella, Pollux, Procyon, and Sirius.

Capella

Auriga

Taurus

Pollux

Gemini

Aldebaran

Procyon

Orion

Rigel

Sirius

The Satellite Cluster (NGC 2244) through a telescope

DIFFICULTY ●●○○○

This small, but beautiful, constellation rests across from the handle of the Big Dipper. Corona Borealis means "Northern Crown", in Latin. This constellation boasts seven bright stars, arching through a curve like knights at a round table.

Corona Borealis

This bright star is officially called Alphekka, but it also goes by the name Gemma, which mean "Jewel" in Latin.

Can you spot the Big Dipper?

Boötes

The constellation Boötes looks like a giant ice cream cone located next to the Big Dipper, though traditionally this constellation is depicted as a herdsman. The brightest star is Arcturus, the third brightest star in the sky.

Can you still see Corona Borealis?

In Greek mythology, Boötes represents Arcas, son of Zeus

Boötes

The North Star

Arcturus

The Big Dipper

Izar is a binary star, but may require a telescope with a diameter of three or four inches to resolve the two individual stars.

DIFFICULTY ●●○○○

Leo

Leo, the Lion, is a spring constellation, that to me looks like a mouse. Some people recognize Leo by a question mark shaped pattern known as "the Sickle". The brightest star in this constellation is Regulus.

Leo

Regulus

The Sickle

DIFFICULTY ●●●●○

Nicknamed the "Hamburger Galaxy" (NGC 3628), this galaxy is part of the "Leo Trio", a group of galaxies viewable together through a small telescope in extremely dark skies.

Here are Pollux and Castor in Gemini, hiding low in the springtime sky

You may want to lie on your back for this one. To find the constellation, start by identifying its brightest star, Spica. To do this, start with the Big Dipper, then "Arc to Arcturus", a red star, then spike (or speed) to Spica.

In Greek mythology, Virgo represents the goddess of justice

Arc to Arcturus, then Spike to Spica

Arcturus

Virgo

Spica

The Diamond

DIFFICULTY ● ● ● ○ ○

Globular Cluster M3 is only slightly dimmer than M13 in Hercules!

Can you still see Leo?

Cancer & the Beehive

The stars in this constellation aren't very bright, making Cancer a difficult constellation to identify.

However, in the center of Cancer lies an object called "the Beehive" (M44), a very popular target for small telescopes and binoculars.

Cancer means "the Crab" in Latin

Regulus

Cancer

Pollux

Procyon

The Beehive (M44), an open star cluster, almost looks like a constellation within a constellation. It makes a great target for binoculars, too.

DIFFICULTY ●●○○○○

During the summer, Scorpius rises just above the southern horizon. It is easily identified by the claw, and the bright red star, Antares.

The top portion of the constellation forms a star pattern (asterism) sometimes called "the Rake", while the bottom portion is sometimes referred to as "the Longshoreman's Hook".

In Greek mythology, Scorpius is the scorpion that killed Orion

The top star in the Rake, known as Graffias, is a double star when viewed through a telescope

This bright red star, Antares, is often confused with the planet Mars. Antares literally means "anti-Mars"

Scorpius contains many globular clusters, tight groupings of thousands of stars. View these clusters in dark skies. This picture shows globular cluster M4.

DIFFICULTY ●●●○○

SUMMER

Just to the left of Scorpius rests an asterism called "the Teapot", a star pattern within the constellation Sagittarius. This part of the sky is teaming with deep sky objects, and makes for a wonderful area to explore with binoculars.

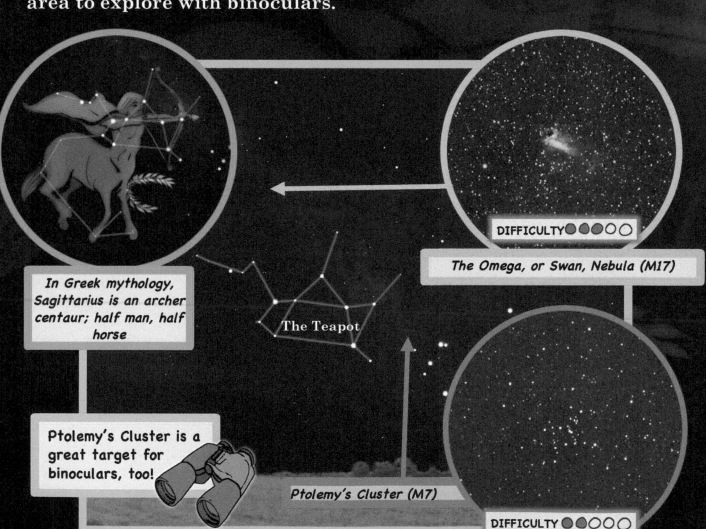

In Greek mythology, Sagittarius is an archer centaur; half man, half horse

The Teapot

The Omega, or Swan, Nebula (M17)

DIFFICULTY ●●●○○

Ptolemy's Cluster is a great target for binoculars, too!

Ptolemy's Cluster (M7)

DIFFICULTY ●○○○○

Like Orion during the winter, Aquila, a summer and fall constellation, is recognized by an alignment of three bright stars. The brightest is Altair, which is bordered by Tarazed, and Alshain.

Vega

Aquila means eagle in Latin. According to Greek mythology, this is the eagle responsible for carrying Zeus's thunderbolts.

The Wild Duck Cluster (M11) is found near the Eagle's tail.

Deneb

Tarazed

Altair

Aquila

Alshain

Aquila is part of the Summer Triangle, a star pattern, or asterism, formed by the bright stars Vega, Deneb, and Altair.

DIFFICULTY ● ● ● ○ ○

The Northern Cross is a star pattern (asterism) located within the constellation Cygnus (the Swan). The brightest star is Deneb, which is also part of the asterism called "the Summer Triangle".

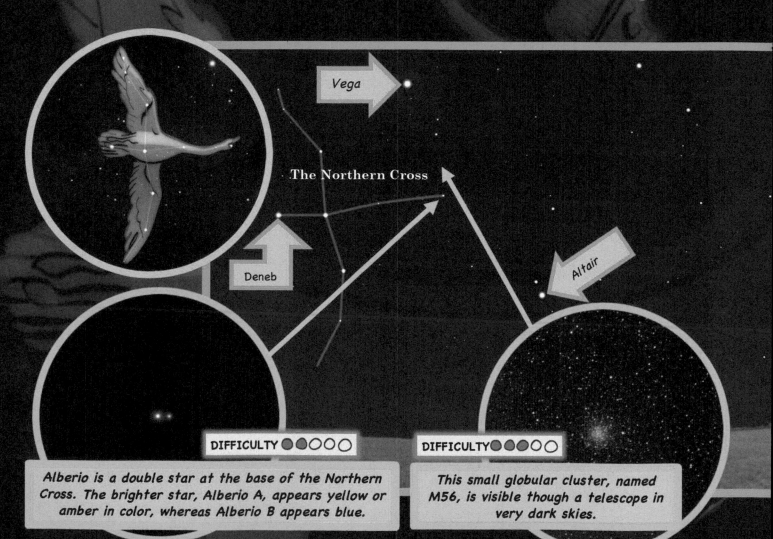

Vega

The Northern Cross

Deneb

Altair

DIFFICULTY ●●○○○

Alberio is a double star at the base of the Northern Cross. The brighter star, Alberio A, appears yellow or amber in color, whereas Alberio B appears blue.

DIFFICULTY ●●●○○

This small globular cluster, named M56, is visible though a telescope in very dark skies.

Lyra, named for a musical instrument called the lyre (a small harp), is easily recognizable in the summer and fall skies by Vega, one of the brightest stars in the sky, and the diamond star pattern that makes up the rest of the constellation.

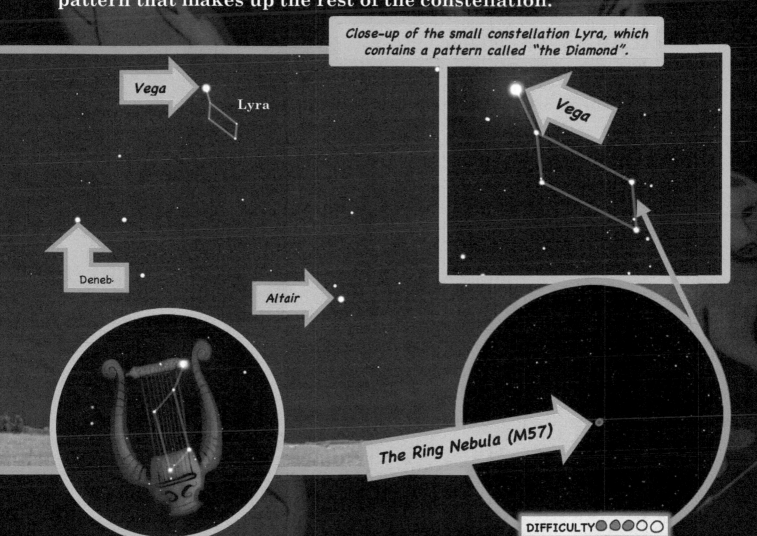

Close-up of the small constellation Lyra, which contains a pattern called "the Diamond".

Vega

Lyra

Vega

Deneb

Altair

The Ring Nebula (M57)

DIFFICULTY ● ● ● ○ ○

After you are able to identify Lyra, Cygnus, and Aquila, it's time to put their brightest stars together in a star pattern known as the Summer Triangle. This combination helps you navigate the night sky, and locate several interesting telescope targets.

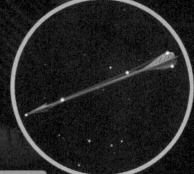

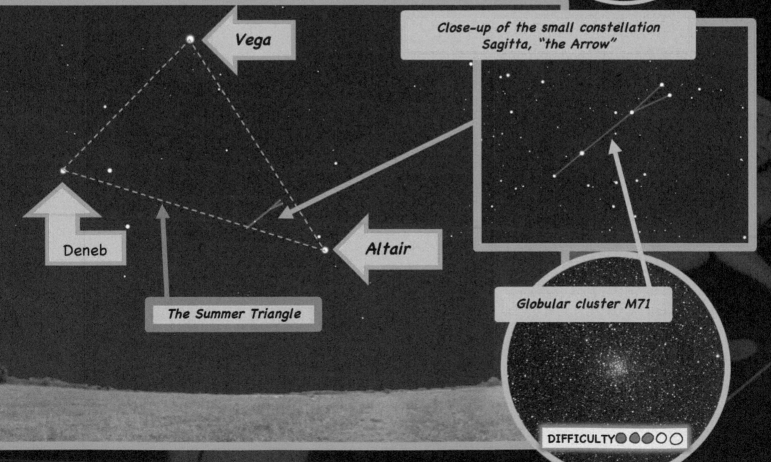

Vega

Close-up of the small constellation Sagitta, "the Arrow"

Deneb

Altair

The Summer Triangle

Globular cluster M71

DIFFICULTY ●●●○○

The Coathanger is a star cluster that rests right on the Summer Triangle. Look for six bright stars lined up in a row, with an additional four stars making up the hook in the hanger.

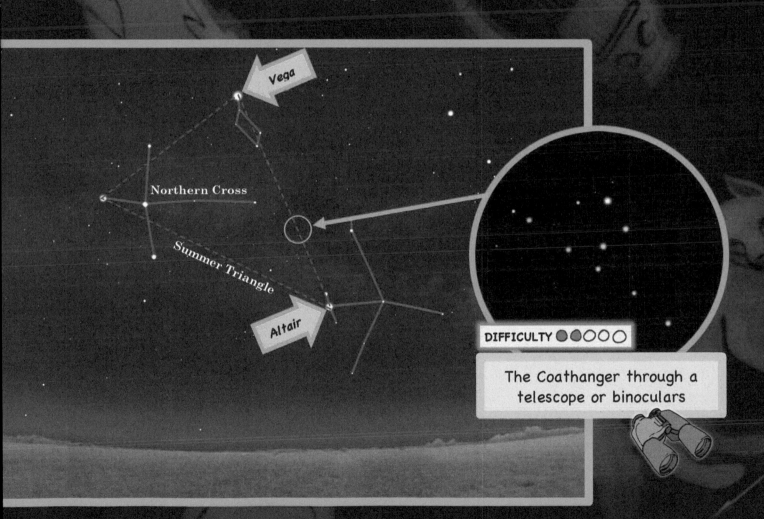

Vega

Northern Cross

Summer Triangle

Altair

DIFFICULTY ●●○○○

The Coathanger through a telescope or binoculars

32

M22 and the Butterfly

Globular cluster M22 (found near the lid of the teapot) and the Butterfly Cluster (found between the teapot and Scorpio's tail) make great targets for binoculars! When viewing the Butterfly through a telescope, you'll need to use your imagination as you picture wings and antenna forming from arcing patterns of stars.

DIFFICULTY ●●○○○○

M22 as viewed through a telescope. This is a great target for binoculars, too.

The Teapot

Scorpio

DIFFICULTY ●●○○○

The Butterfly Cluster (M6) as seen through a telescope.

The Butterfly Cluster (M6) with imaginary lines for the wings and antenna

Sitting above Scorpio and the Teapot, below Hercules, and to the right of the Summer Triangle, Ophiuchus is known more for its lack of central bright stars. It does, however, contain plenty of deep-sky treasures, including: M9, M10, M12, M14, and M107 (all globular clusters).

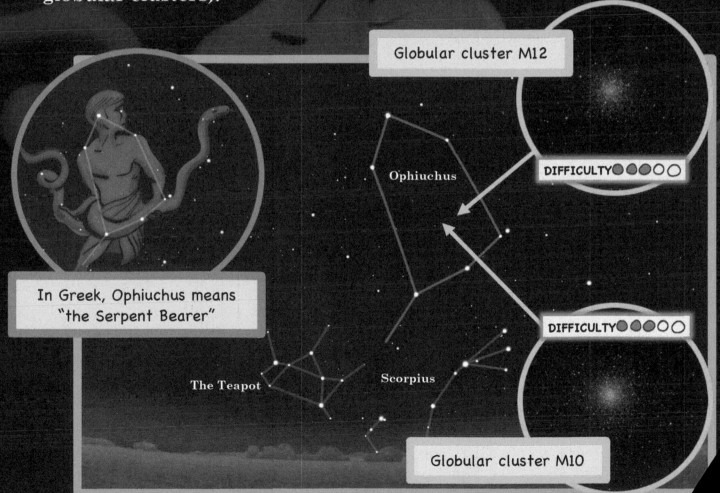

Globular cluster M12

Ophiuchus

DIFFICULTY ◐◐◯◯◯

In Greek, Ophiuchus means "the Serpent Bearer"

DIFFICULTY ◐◐◐◯◯

The Teapot

Scorpius

Globular cluster M10

The Summer Beehive is an open cluster located 1,400 lightyears from Earth. Its collection of bright stars make a wonderful target for binoculars or a small telescope. When observing this cluster, many people see the word "HI" written in the stars. What do you see?

The Summer Triangle

Ophiuchus

Did you know? A light-year is a unit of distance [deter]mined by how far light [travels] in one year

DIFFICULTY ● ● ○ ○ ○ ○

The Summer Beehive (IC4665) through a telescope

The Eagle Nebula is the source of one of the Hubble Space Telescope's most famous images: the Pillars of Creation (right). The constellation, Scutum, in which this nebula is near, is quite dim, so you may need to use the stars in the Teapot and Aquila as a guide.

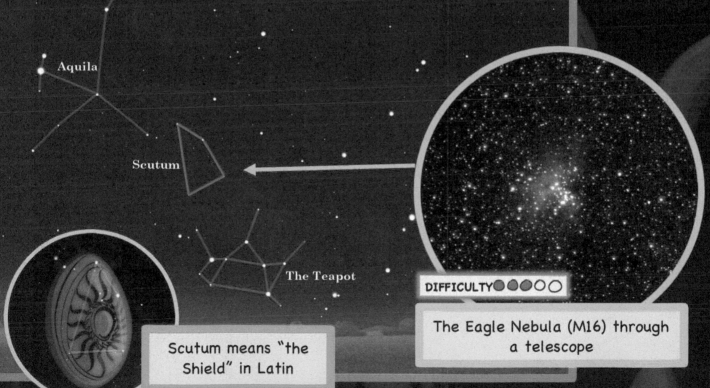

Aquila

Scutum

The Teapot

Scutum means "the Shield" in Latin

DIFFICULTY ●●●○○

The Eagle Nebula (M16) through a telescope

When some stars get old, they blow off their outer layers of gas. The gas is illuminated by the host star. The phenomenon, which we can see through a telescope, is called a planetary nebula.

The Dumbbell Nebula was the first planetary nebula discovered.

Did you know? Nebula means "cloud" in Latin

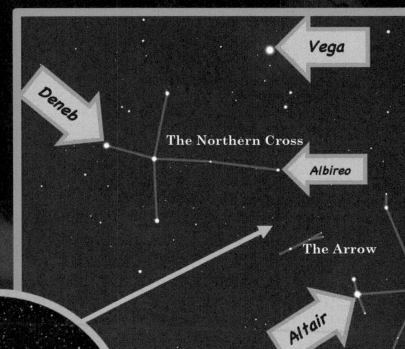

Vega

Deneb

The Northern Cross

Albireo

The Arrow

Altair

The Dumbbell Nebula (M27)

DIFFICULTY ●●●○○

"The Keystone" is an asterism (star pattern) within the summer constellation Hercules. This constellation is dimmer than most of the others, so it helps to find it in reference to other objects, like the bright star, Vega.

The Keystone

Vega

In Greek mythology, Hercules is the immortal son of Zeus

"The Great Globular Cluster in Hercules" (M13) is one of the brightest globular clusters. It is also easy to find between two corners of the keystone.

Can you still see the Summer Triangle?

DIFFICULTY ●●○○○

Pegasus is located on the opposite side of Cassiopeia from the North Star. The square, or "Box", is an asterism (a pattern of stars that isn't a constellation). While the box itself is devoid of popular stargazing targets, it can be used as a guide to find nearby targets, such as the Andromeda and Triangulum galaxies.

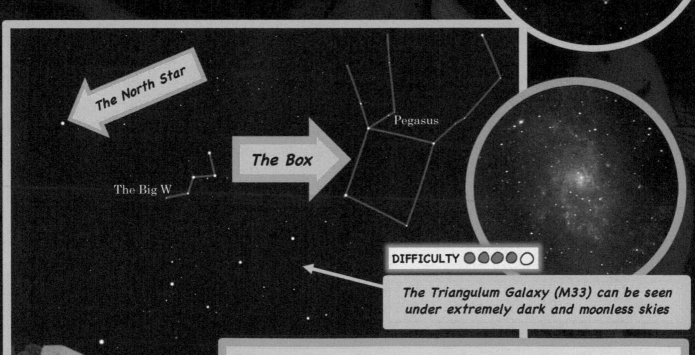

The North Star

The Big W

The Box

Pegasus

DIFFICULTY ⬤⬤⬤⬤◯

The Triangulum Galaxy (M33) can be seen under extremely dark and moonless skies

Remember! Objects in the night sky appear to rotate around the North Star. Depending on the time of night, and time of year, Pegasus may appear to the right, left, or above the North Star.

At only two million light-years away, the Andromeda Galaxy is the nearest galaxy to Earth (with the noted exception of dwarf galaxies).

In dark skies, this galaxy is visible even without a telescope. To find it, use the Big W to identify reference stars in the constellation Andromeda.

The North Star

The Big W

Andromeda

DIFFICULTY ●●○○○

The Andromeda Galaxy (M31) as it would appear through a small telescope

This galaxy is a great target for binoculars, too!

Did you know? As summer turns into autumn, the days get shorter, and the stars come out earlier. For this reason, many of the summer constellations can be seen well into the fall!

These two clusters, designated NGC 869 and NGC 884, are visible to the naked eye in extremely dark skies. However, in a telescope, they're a magnificent sight in almost all conditions (unless there are clouds).

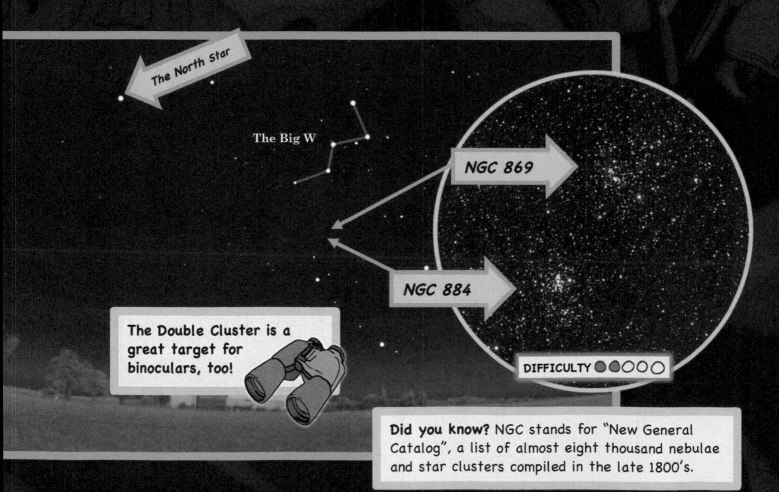

The North Star

The Big W

NGC 869

NGC 884

The Double Cluster is a great target for binoculars, too!

DIFFICULTY ●●○○○

Did you know? NGC stands for "New General Catalog", a list of almost eight thousand nebulae and star clusters compiled in the late 1800's.

AUTUMN

Cepheus (Iris Nebula)

Near the square in the constellation Cepheus you'll find the Iris Nebula. This is a reflection nebula, where a nearby star illuminates interstellar dust.

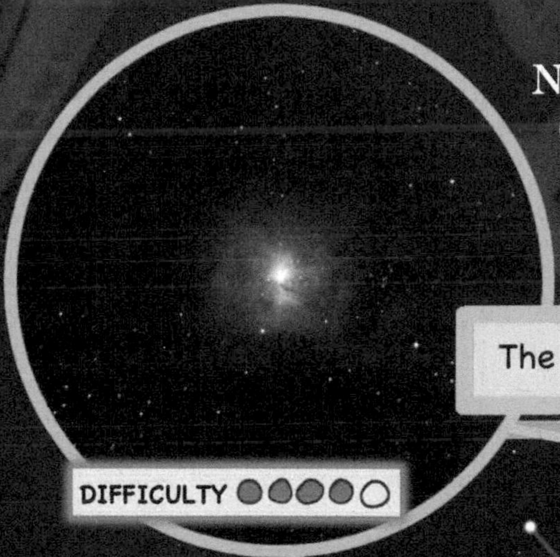

The Iris Nebula (NGC 7023)

DIFFICULTY ●●●●○

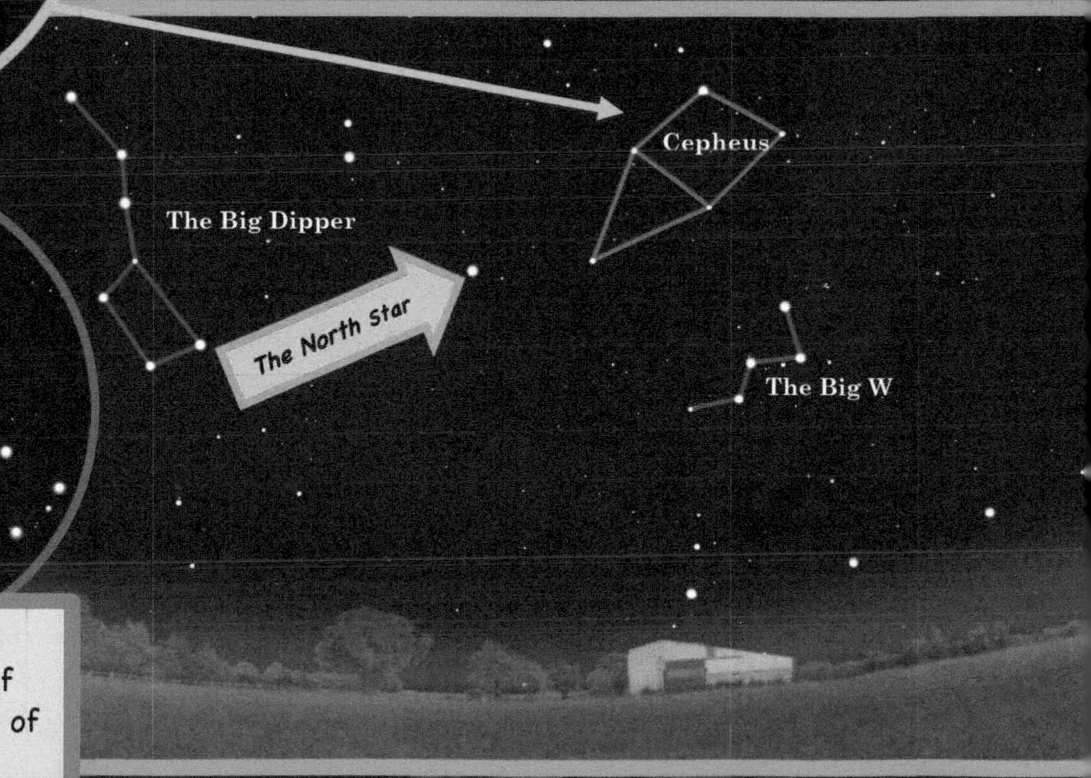

Cepheus
The Big Dipper
The North Star
The Big W

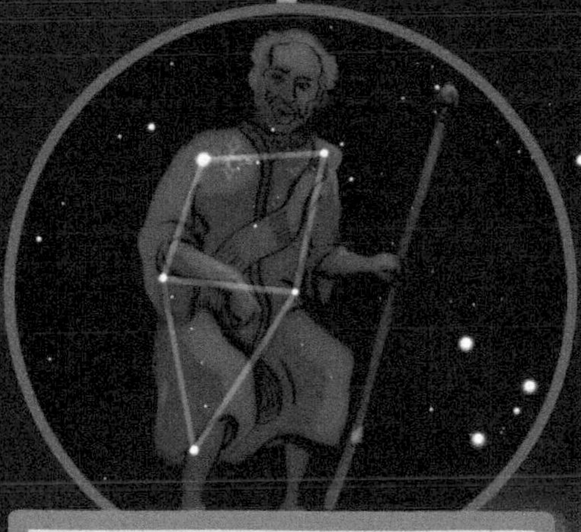

In Greek mythology, Cepheus is the king of Aethiopia, and husband of Cassiopeia

Check Stellarium

Due to Mercury's extreme proximity to the Sun, it can be challenging to get a good look at it. It may only appear in the evening sky a few days per year.

Because this planet is closer to the Sun than Earth, careful and frequent observation will reveal that Mercury has phases like the Moon!

Did you know? In astronomy, Mercury and Venus are called the "Inferior Planets" because they are closer to the Sun than the Earth.

Mercury through a small telescope

This image of Mercury was taken during a flyby by an unmanned NASA spacecraft called "Messenger"

DIFFICULTY ●●●○○

Mercury can be a challenge to see with your telescope because it is visible for only a few weeks per year, in the evening sky

Due to its proximity to the Sun, Venus only appears shortly after sunset and shortly before sunrise.

Just like Mercury, this planet is closer to the Sun than the Earth, and has phases like the Moon! Because Venus appears white through a telescope, some people momentarily think they're looking at the Moon.

This image of Venus was taken by the unmanned NASA spacecraft "Mariner 10"

Did you know? Venus is named after the Roman goddess of Love and Beauty

DIFFICULTY ● ○ ○ ○ ○

Venus as it appears through a small telescope (notice how it almost looks like the Moon?)

While the average surface temperature on Mars is around minus 55 degrees Celsius, temperatures around the equator can rise to around 20 degrees. With a day only 37 minutes longer than on Earth, Mars is considered a prime location for human exploration, later this century. This doesn't mean humans will be able to go exploring without a spacesuit; Mars only has 1% the atmospheric pressure of Earth.

At the time of this writing, NASA has been continuously operating robotic rovers on the surface of Mars for the last 20 years.

Mars is the fourth planet from the sun, and only a six-month journey via spaceship. However, as of 2017, only robotic spacecraft have visited.

NASA's Curiosity Rover

Mars through a telescope

Under ideal conditions, you may be able to see Mars' polar ice caps, and varying hues of red and brown. However, most of the time, through a telescope, Mars will look like a bright red star.

DIFFICULTY ●●○○○

Jupiter is the largest planet in our Solar System. It is more massive than all of the other planets put together. Jupiter's four brightest moons, discovered by Galileo Galilei in 1610, are visible in even the smallest telescopes, and binoculars, too. Through your telescope, you should also see at least two cloud belts. If you're lucky, and have a slightly larger telescope, you may be able to see the "Great Red Spot".

The "Great Red Spot" is a storm that has been raging on Jupiter for at least hundreds of years

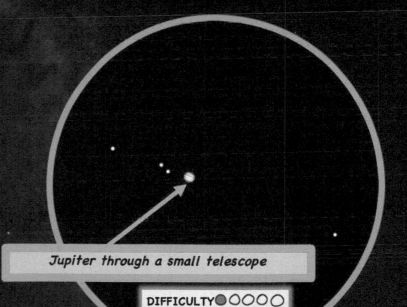

Jupiter through a small telescope

DIFFICULTY ●○○○○

The Galilean Moons

Check Stellarium

Jupiter's four largest moons (called the Galilean Moons) change position every night, so you'll need to use astronomy software to help you determine which moon is which.

Jupiter's Moons

DIFFICULTY ●○○○○

Ganymede is the largest moon in the solar system, having over twice the mass of Earth's moon.

Europa is the smallest of the four Galilean moons. Latest estimates project that beneath an icy surface, there is an ocean over 60 miles deep.

Callisto has the lowest radiation levels of Jupiter's large moons, and thus, would make a promising location for human settlement.

Io orbits most closely to Jupiter. It sports over four hundred active volcanoes! Due to the amount of volcanic activity, Io's surface features frequently change. Io has almost no meteor craters because lava fills them soon after they are formed.

Saturn is probably the single most fantastic thing that can be seen through a small telescope. Its majestic gold and brown hue is enough to take one's breath away.

At its closest, Saturn is over one billion kilometers from Earth. NASA's latest Saturn probe, named Cassini, took six years and nine months to reach this planet.

Saturn through a telescope

DIFFICULTY ●○○○○

This image of Saturn was taken during a flyby by an unmanned NASA spacecraft called "Cassini"

On most nights, you should be able to see Saturn's largest moon, Titan. But on really clear nights, or with larger telescopes, you should be able to see several other moons, like Rhea, Dione, and Tethys.

Despite the lack of visible details, Uranus has several interesting features. This planet has thirteen narrow, yet distinct, rings (these rings are only visible in professional telescopes like the Hubble Space Telescope).

Uranus also has 27 known moons. If you have a fairly large telescope, you may be able to see the brightest five: Titania, Oberon, Ariel, Umbriel, and Miranda.

Despite looking very small through the average telescope, you should be able to make out the distinct blue-green disk.

DIFFICULTY ○○○○○

At it's closest, Neptune is a whopping 2.7 billion miles distant. That's four hours at the speed of light! It's orbit is so wide, that it takes 165 years for this planet to orbit the Sun. Neptune has an average temperature of minus 214 Celsius, whereas Uranus averages minus 216 Celsius. This is why these planets are nicknamed the "Ice Giants".

Neptune has thirteen known moons, the largest of which is called Triton.

Through a telescope, Neptune is clearly blue. You should also be able to see Triton, Neptune's largest moon.

DIFFICULTY●●●●●

You might be wondering why Pluto doesn't have its own section in this book. That's because Pluto is so small and so dim, that it is extremely challenging for amateur astronomers to observe.

Comets

Nicknamed "dirty snowballs", comets are made mainly of ice and dust. When comets are near the Sun, they release gas as dust in the form of a long (and sometimes colorful) tail. When a bright comet is visible from Earth, it usually makes the news. However, they can be difficult to see, so it helps to use binoculars or a telescope.

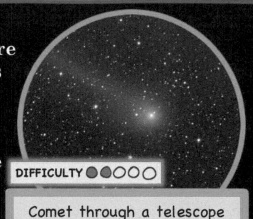

DIFFICULTY ●●○○○

Comet through a telescope

Comet PANSTARRS (C/2011) viewed without a telescope

Comets are great targets for binoculars, too!

Comet 67P imaged by the European Space Agency's Rosetta Spacecraft

WINTER CONSTELLATION MAP

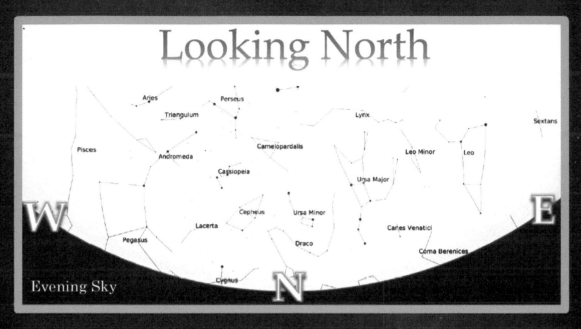

Looking North

Evening Sky

Aries
Perseus
Triangulum
Lynx
Sextans
Pisces
Camelopardalis
Leo Minor
Leo
Andromeda
Cassiopeia
Ursa Major
Cepheus
Ursa Minor
Lacerta
Canes Venatici
Pegasus
Draco
Coma Berenices
Cygnus

W · E · N

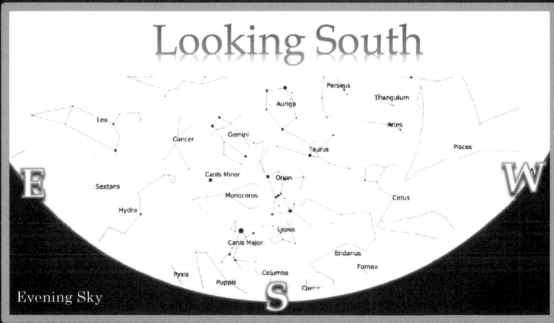

Looking South

Evening Sky

Perseus
Auriga
Triangulum
Leo
Aries
Cancer
Gemini
Pisces
Taurus
Canis Minor
Orion
Sextans
Monoceros
Cetus
Hydra
Lepus
Canis Major
Eridanus
Pyxis
Fornax
Puppis
Columba
Caelum

E · W · S

SPRING CONSTELLATION MAP

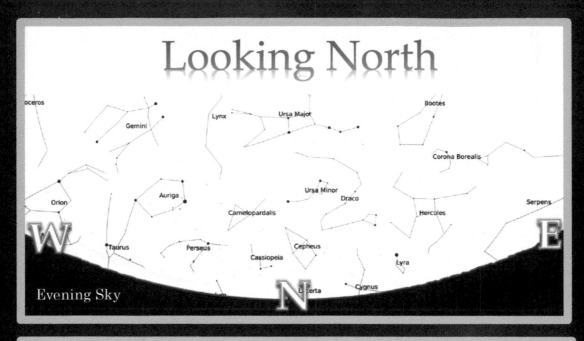

Looking North

Evening Sky

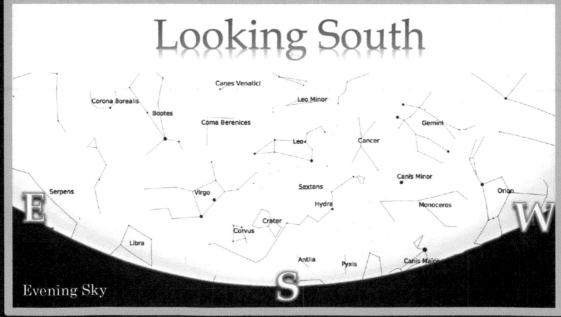

Looking South

Evening Sky

SUMMER CONSTELLATION MAP

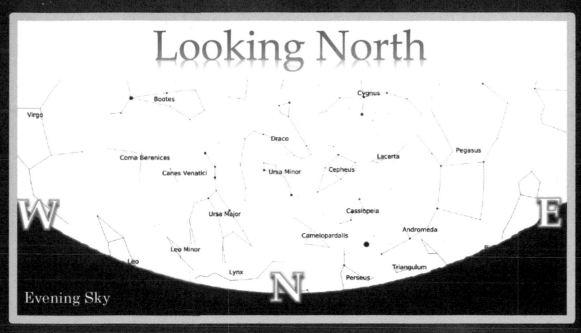

Looking North

Virgo
Bootes
Cygnus
Draco
Coma Berenices
Lacerta
Pegasus
Canes Venatici
Ursa Minor
Cepheus
Ursa Major
Cassiopeia
W
E
Camelopardalis
Andromeda
Leo Minor
Leo
Lynx
Triangulum
Perseus
N

Evening Sky

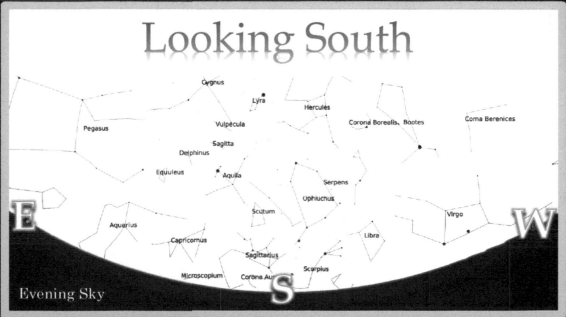

Looking South

Cygnus
Lyra
Hercules
Corona Borealis Bootes
Coma Berenices
Pegasus
Vulpecula
Sagitta
Delphinus
Equuleus
Aquila
Serpens
Ophiuchus
Virgo
E
W
Aquarius
Scutum
Capricornus
Libra
Sagittarius
Scorpius
Microscopium
Corona Au...
S

Evening Sky

AUTUMN CONSTELLATION MAP

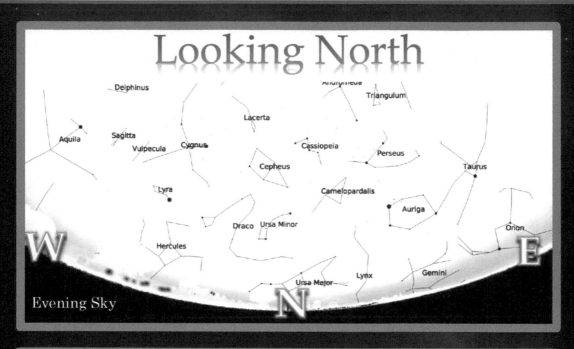

Looking North

Evening Sky

Delphinus
Andromeda
Triangulum
Lacerta
Sagitta
Aquila
Vulpecula
Cygnus
Cassiopeia
Perseus
Cepheus
Taurus
Lyra
Camelopardalis
Auriga
Draco
Ursa Minor
Orion
Hercules
E
W
Lynx
Gemini
Ursa Major
N

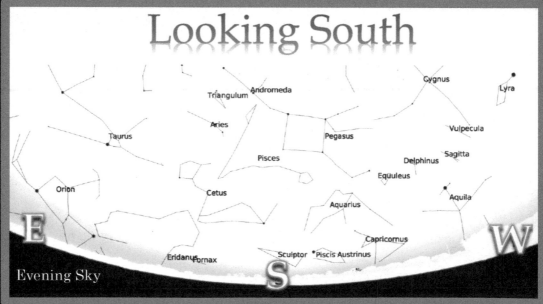

Looking South

Evening Sky

Cygnus
Lyra
Triangulum
Andromeda
Aries
Vulpecula
Taurus
Pegasus
Sagitta
Pisces
Delphinus
Equuleus
Orion
Cetus
Aquarius
Aquila
E
Capricornus
W
Eridanus
Fornax
Sculptor
Piscis Austrinus
S

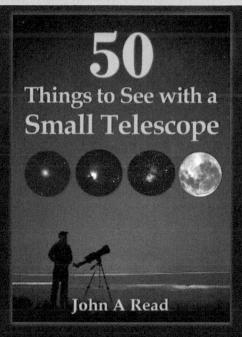

50 Things to See with a Small Telescope focuses on the most popular targets viewed at stargazing events around the world. Though there is substantial overlap with the kid's edition, the book is still a great stargazing tool, providing even more fun facts about each object.

50 Targets for the Mid-Sized Telescope introduces the beginner stargazer to an assortment of astronomical wonders. With detailed, yet easy to follow star maps, unique for each target and season, the budding astronomer will explore the universe like never before.